CHISEL-TOOTH, THE BEAVER

By the Same Author

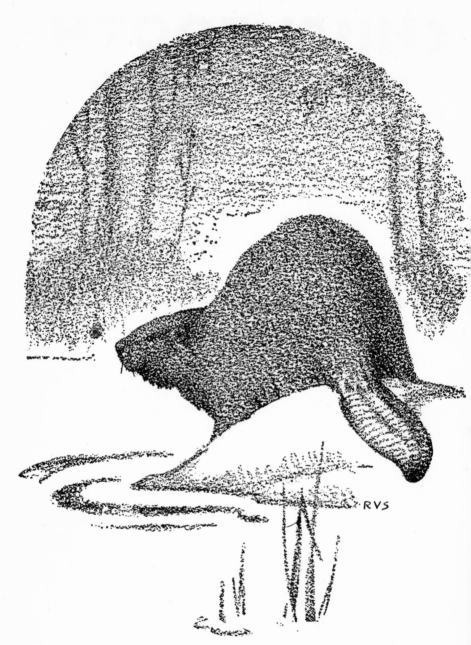

SILENTLY HE PLODDED THROUGH THE FOG

CHISEL-TOOTH
THE BEAVER

by

JOSEPH WHARTON LIPPINCOTT

Illustrated by **ROLAND V. SHUTTS**

J. B. LIPPINCOTT COMPANY
Philadelphia—New York—London

In memory of the Grandfather who many years ago taught me the meaning of that plain little phrase:—" to work like a beaver."

PREFACE

WHEN North America was still a wilderness the beavers lived in nearly all the lakes and streams as far south as Mexico. The red man depended upon them for food and robes, and grew to like and admire the gentle, industrious little animals so deeply that he wove them into his legends as creatures almost sacred.

The white man had seen beavers in England, Europe and Asia, but had begun to exterminate them for their valuable fur by the time that the first settlers came to America and discovered there what seemed to be an inexhaustible new supply. It was not very long before trappers were everywhere penetrating the wilderness, killing beavers and bringing back their pelts for sale or barter. The red man often was bribed to help.

Spurred by greed, the red man and the white fought over the possession of the beavers. Tribes and even nations glared at each other, and when ships laden with pelts sailed across the Atlantic they sometimes were captured by enemy vessels and the valuable cargoes stolen. Even the huge new wilderness could not bear this for long—here too the beavers were being exterminated!

But why all this fuss about the beaver? In the first place his fur, beneath the long guard hairs, is short, thick, lasting and very warm and beautiful. Women wanted it for all manner of wraps, and men used it for coat linings and, most of all, for their stylish high hats. Then, too, the beaver carried two glands which yielded castoreum, a substance having an interesting odd odor and greatly prized for a variety of medicinal uses. It was only natural that such a clean animal, living in the purest running water and eating bark, leaves and roots, would have very palatable flesh. And lastly, he was easy to locate and catch.

Only just in time, both Canada and the United States awoke to save him from complete annihilation. It was shown he did little real harm. Indeed, on the contrary, the ponds he built checked erosion and floods and, by conserving water, lessened the dangers from drought and increased the supply of fish and waterfowl. Some of the farmers' most productive meadows along the edge of streams have been found to be the bottoms of old, discarded beaver ponds where silt and loam, washed down by rains, collected year after year to make soil many feet deep.

The beaver, like the rabbit, the squirrel and the mouse, is a rodent. Indeed, he resembles an overgrown meadow mouse with a strange leather paddle for a tail. But, for rapid swimming, his hind feet are large and webbed, and his front feet like small hands that can be tucked out of sight as he kicks his way easily through the water. He

PREFACE

can close his nose, also his ears, when he dives, and he can keep his beautiful fur in perfect order by combing it with his toes, particularly the second toe on each hind foot, which has a split nail used for this purpose.

The map is dotted with towns and streams bearing his name in lasting memory of the days of his greatness. But let us study him and provide that he will always be with us in more than memory, shyly swimming out of his mud house in the stillness of evening to cut wood and build his dams, his roads and little canals in the seclusion of our remaining forests.

J. W. L.

CONTENTS

ILLUSTRATIONS

15

CHISEL-TOOTH, THE BEAVER

RVS

I

THE STRANGER

Perhaps Tinker's Creek had never before seen anything like the large, furry, brown animal that one night in June waddled along its narrow course. A cautious creature, it swam wherever there was enough water in which to do this, and always it hesitated for a minute or two before leaving a pool, as if fearful that some enemy would waylay it among the rocks where it was not so much at home.

At the site of a lumberman's old deserted dam where the ends of timbers still were visible, this strange animal

stopped to look around. The more closely it examined
the remains of what once had been such a good water
stop, the more excited it became. Climbing at length on
a broad rock for a better view, it sat up on its hind legs
in the manner of a begging dog and looked long and ear-
nestly on all sides. In the pale moonlight it was easily
visible to the bats that flew close to the water after insects, but they took little notice of it, and the other little
animals were busy with their own affairs; so none knew
what was going on in the brain of this furry one as it sat
on the stone, nor what tremendous changes were to happen in consequence of its coming.

For this was a beaver, greatest of all animal engineers,
whose ancestors had built dams on such creeks as this long
before the coming of the white man, even long before the
Indian. This one was a young male ousted by older and
stronger beaver from a lodge in a pond several miles
down the valley. Had he not been born with an adventurous spirit he never would have made his way this far up
Tinker's Creek, particularly as he had left behind him the
most lovely little lady beaver he had ever seen.

It was partly because of jealousy in regard to her that
he had been forced to leave the pond, for several other
males were noticing her charms and resenting the fact
that she was beginning to show a marked liking for the
company of this adventurous, not yet fully grown, two-
year-old youngster. So here he was, all alone in a place

entirely new to him and packed with dangers because of the lack of a den and ponds in which he could dive and hide.

Small wonder that he sniffed the damp air continually for any scent that might betray a sneaking lynx or other enemy. His life, so far, had always depended upon his wariness and his speed in reaching deep water and hiding in it.

The beaver's thoughts however were wandering. Instinct was making him wish to start a dam across the narrow gorge, piling up this shallow creek water and making a pond in which he could swim and live and be safe.

And so he was dreaming dreams, there in the moonlight with the little brown bats flitting about his head.

A shadow passed across the sky. At least it seemed like a shadow, but in reality it was a great horned owl, a hungry old fellow, flapping slowly over the trees to have a better look at the brown lump on the stone. A beaver was big game for such as he, too big to handle safely, but he had caught young ones and was just reckless enough to think of risking a fight for his dinner that night.

The brown lump remained perfectly still as the owl circled. Only too well the beaver knew that the slightest motion would have made the big bird sure that he was not part of the stone. Again the suspicious owl came silently sailing overhead, looking hard and dipping alarmingly close. A quiver passed through the brown lump; the owl saw it, turned as if on a pivot and spread his talons.

Instantly the beaver rushed for the shelter of the old timbers, fairly hurling his body over the rocks. He looked bigger to the owl then, much too formidable. The bird checked himself in the air. Under the beams plunged his quarry, and the great owl flapped upwards again. Just because the beaver had run away from him, he was so excited that he flew around and around, then hid in a tree and solemnly sat in wait. But he saw no more of the wary, flat-tailed one, so at length, hearing a hoot or two from his mate in the distance, he hooted in reply and flew away to join her and hunt for much smaller game.

But under the timbers dirt was flying. The beaver was digging himself in, making a burrow in which he could be more safe. The fierce old owl, though not nearly as heavy and strong as he, had given him a scare and he was getting ready for all enemies. At every hoot in the distance more dirt flew.

Many years had passed since this old dam had held back the waters of the little creek. In the days when sawmills in Pennsylvania were still cutting up big hemlock logs from forests never before thinned by the hand of man, Tinker's Pond was a famous place. Si Tinker and his brothers had made the pond by building this dam across the gorge at its narrowest point. The timbers

THE BEAVER RUSHED FOR THE SHELTER OF THE TIMBERS

checked the flow of Tinker's Creek between the mountains and caused the water to spread over a basin a hundred yards wide and nearly a mile long.

By means of this pond Si Tinker had floated logs from rocky places where horses could scarcely find a footing, to the beginning of the chute down which they were made to go rolling, sliding and thundering to the very door of a sawmill in the lower valley.

But when the big timber had been cut and carried away, Tinker's Pond lost most of its usefulness to mankind. As soon as Si and his brothers found it hard to earn a living up in the mountains, they deserted their snug little log cabins and moved down to the mill in the valley. Soon, however, that too had to be abandoned for

25

lack of any good wood to saw. First the mosses, then briars and ferns and last of all young trees, spread over the paths; and when the log houses crumbled apart, they in their turn were covered with greenery and almost completely hidden.

Tinker's Pond, once so important, soon was buried in the new growth and almost forgotten by man. Then, one night in early spring, a big rain deluged the mountains and sent such a wild mass of water rushing over the dam that the rotting old timbers suddenly gave way and were scattered in every direction. Fish, turtles and eels by the dozen were carried away with the water. Once again Tinker's Creek flowed in its narrow channel through the basin, though now acres of fresh black mud surrounded it.

This bare, ugly stretch of earth was like a challenge to the forest. And before spring had chased the frost out of the ground the forest had answered by spreading seeds of its grasses, weeds, vines and trees all over the bare places. Every time the wind blew, dry seeds would be shaken out of cones or from the stems on which they had grown. They were sent flying about, the lightest and those with wings to help them float, going the farthest. They could not guide themselves toward the inviting mud, but those which happened to alight upon it stuck there, and in the thaws and rains were taken into it, just as if planted by man. These began to throw out roots as soon as the ground grew warm enough to wake them into life.

26

In April there was a delicate greenish tinge, in May a decided fuzz of green on the black. By autumn the bare bottom of Tinker's Pond looked like a meadow.

The mud which at first was so soft that it had easily been washed into the creek by every hard rain, now was so full of roots that it could resist even the attack of the thunderstorms that swept the mountains and soaked the basin. The vines had spread by sending trailers over the ground, while the grasses and many of the weeds had done their part in the race by thrusting shoots through the soil in all directions. The vines easily held the lead at first, but the more slowly plodding grasses and weeds soon had begun to catch up.

So rich and deep was this mud which had been washed from the mountainsides by many rains and then been added to by each autumn's falling leaves, that the whole place quickly became a tangle of green growing things, each striving to shoot up fast enough to catch its share of the life-giving sunlight, toward which all were reaching out their leaves. The slow growers were overshadowed, cut off from the light, and gradually killed, leaving the battle for life to the strongest among the quick growing trees. So the bottom of Tinker's Pond changed in a few years from a grassy pasture to a bramble thicket and then to a young forest of poplar, pine, hemlock, birch, maple, oak and beech.

In the middle wound the creek just as before. But it

was not much of a stream during the dry days of summer, sometimes not much more than a little brook which connected a few deep pools.

Animals visited the place. Among them were a deer or two, a few rabbits and gray squirrels, one pair of brown mink and a black and white skunk. Then there were the Tinker's Creek raccoon, a smart red fox, a sleepy old woodchuck and almost endless little creatures

such as mice, shrews and moles. Occasionally other animals made visits or passed through, among these being some of the beaver's worst enemies, whom he was soon to meet and know.

The birds delighted in the place. Largest of all was the bald eagle who could soar over the mountains so easily. But there were wild turkeys too, and a number of ruffed grouse, crows, hawks, owls and herons, in addition to smaller birds such as the hard-working woodpeckers.

Around the water were other creatures; frogs, snakes, turtles. And in the creek itself swam trout, dace, eels and chub. Crayfish which looked like little lobsters made burrows under the flat stones in the shallows.

As yet the beaver had noticed only a few of these. He was not a meat eater and felt no grudge against other creatures. However, though he had had little experience, he feared the big killers such as the lynx. Their unpleasant scent and their looks warned him that they were dangerous. But now the world looked peaceful and very beautiful. Food grew on all sides; and water, so beloved by all his kind, flowed gently beneath his very nose.

With a sudden burst of joy from his heart he ran along the bank to a thick, white barked birch and, reaching high, bit it with his long teeth, cutting the soft wood and leaving two lines from the left and two more from the right, the sign of the beaver—his mark.

II

DIGGING IN

THE beaver was digging again. Every two or three minutes he backed part of the way out of the burrow to sniff and listen. The woods seemed very still, and yet there were countless little sounds that his ears could detect. Two white-footed mice were playing in the leaves, running about gaily and squeaking in mock quarrels. Overhead a flying squirrel on a limb was tearing an old pine cone to bits and dropping the pieces; these pattered on the ground below. Whenever the little animal came to a seed the pattering stopped while she ate it.

Once a twig snapped. At the sound the beaver

30

straightened up and gave all of his attention to finding out what kind of heavy creature was so near. Was it a friendly woods animal or an enemy? Presently the scent of a deer came to him on the soft night air and he was no longer worried; deer, not being meat eaters, were harmless things. It was not very long after this, however, when a scent reached his nostrils which told him that a real enemy was coming, a lynx or bobcat, the stealthy, soft-footed killer that the furry ones always feared. Only a bear could dare feel safe with him about. Silently the beaver crept in to the very end of the hole, turned himself around to face the entrance and then waited and watched. Even with the smell of fresh, wet earth all around him he could scent the big cat.

The smell grew stronger, then lessened and at last faded away. The prowling cat passed stealthily down the valley without noticing any sign of the new arrival at Tinker's old dam.

After waiting long enough to make sure that all was well, the beaver crept out, looked around and then recommenced the digging. This time he worked even faster and began to make the tunnel lead upwards among the tree roots. If one of these interfered, he cut through it with his front teeth, nipped it off and carried the piece to the entrance where it could be dropped out of the way. Several times he tried to eat the outer covering of a root, but this was bitter enough to discourage him. Small

31

stones he kicked or shoved out, but larger ones he carried, or dragged with his teeth and front paws.

Before the light of day spread over the mountains he had tunnelled ten feet into the soft ground and then hollowed out a small room in which to sleep. Now he felt more safe. Squatting in his dark little chamber he licked his earth-spattered coat and combed and polished it with his feet. But a swim in one of the pools did him even more good, the water loosening all of the remaining dirt while not entering his very thick, slightly oily fur.

Now it was time to eat before going to bed; so with many halts and much caution he clambered along the bank of the stream, munching tender shoots, the bark of small maples and some swamp weeds that had a pleasant scent. Then, while the red rays of the rising sun climbed up the mountainsides, he scuttled back to the burrow by way of the stream bed, spread the newly dug earth piles more evenly, looked around with something like real satisfaction and dove into his tunnel to stretch out and sleep on the soft mattress made by his own fur coat.

Wrens and thrushes looked with curiosity into the burrow's mouth, and a dark brown water snake curled itself on a sun-baked rock nearby, but neither they nor the robins, vireos and other birds and four-footed creatures that moved about during the day knew anything of their new neighbor so snugly hidden underground.

DIGGING IN

When daylight no longer showed in the tunnel, the beaver stretched, scratched his head and finally came out. After a long look at his surroundings, he made up his mind that there was nothing to worry him, so he proceeded upstream for an evening meal. Soon he was back again examining the pool in front of his burrow and testing with his weight the stones and timbers lying about. Occasionally he dragged a stick or a piece of wood into the stream current and anchored it below the pool, and often he cut a green bush or a very young tree and pulled that to the same place.

Gradually a line of such things was arranged across the stream in a half circle. Among this litter some sods, stones, weeds and chunks of mud were deposited with care and firmly wedged, the beaver watching the effect on the water and always trying to stop its flow past the pool.

The creek became more placid, the pool slightly larger. The wet earth in the bottom of the burrow grew more moist. But one night was not enough time in which to build even a very small dam; several more were required before the water rose a few inches. After that the job was easier, because the silent worker could partly float sticks across the pool and to the places where they were needed. Green bushes were arranged with the twigs pointing downstream so that they caught and propped firmly against the stones and would not easily be pushed along by the flowing water. The thick ends pointing upstream were firmly weighted down with layers of mud and roots.

The beaver carried sods and mud clasped between his front feet and his chest, while he swam with his hind feet and balanced with his big flat tail. To poke the things into place he used his nose and his front feet.

As soon as the low entrance to his burrow was under the surface of the water he stopped work on the dam. Now, indeed, he had a beautifully hidden den which he could swim into from the pool. The far end where he slept was well above the level of the water. None but a water animal would suspect the presence of the burrow or dive under the surface to hunt for it, so the furry little engineer felt safe enough; he relaxed, fed more freely, explored.

But now, with all urgent work finished, he had time to be lonely and to fret because he missed the happy companionship of the busy colony in the stream below. Several times he started down the creek to pay them a visit, but always he was stopped by some danger scent or sound. At length there came a rainy, warm night with mist in deep layers over the stream. Purposefully he climbed his little dam and clambered down the rocky road by which he had come. All that he could think of was the desire to reach the old home and again be among his own kind.

Silently he plodded, sometimes in water only up to his

round stomach, sometimes in moss and fern-rimmed pools that ended in tiny waterfalls and rocky stretches. He ran himself almost out of breath but kept on.

Had a bobcat been prowling up Tinker's Creek that night he could scarcely have pierced the fog with his eyes or heard the furry body that eased itself so gently over loose rocks and in and out of the water. The rain which kept the prowlers under cover could not hurt the beaver's dense fur. Later, when a heavier shower cleared away the fog, he was at the very edge of the old beaver pond sniffing the scent of his relatives on stone and log and mud bank.

Soon he was in deeper water, swimming. Only his head showed as he cut the surface at the right speed to leave scarcely a ripple. In front of him on a point of land was a big pile of sticks and earth. This was the beaver house in which he had been raised and where he had left his mother and her latest newborn litter of four. He knew very well where to dive to reach the main entrance that led from the floor of the pond to a snug room inside, above the water level.

But first he lay still, on the surface of the pond, and listened.

III

VISITING HOME

S<small>OUND</small> carries clearly over still water. The beaver heard gnawing of bark to the left, scraping of logs to the right, a splash ahead and the soft ripple that denotes a swimming animal. All of these were natural sounds in an undisturbed beaver pond.

He waited. The fog was lifting and allowing more light from the sky to reach the water. With his eyes distended to their utmost he could see the shore on both sides and, ahead, the edge of the dam. Something was moving across the dam, a small animal that hopped instead of trotting or walking. That, the beaver knew, would be just a cottontail rabbit, using the dam for a bridge. Two heads came out of the shadows on the water, one followed the other, both moving fast along the surface, their bodies entirely under water. Too small for beaver; these were muskrats.

A splash to the left! The beaver's eyes being almost on the top of his floating head he could see in that direction too. A piece of white barked wood was apparently slipping of its own accord into the pond. But in front of it appeared a flat brown lump, a beaver's head. The piece of wood was being dragged by one end, into the water and then toward the dam.

The skillful way in which the animal moved the three-foot log, and the size of its head, which was larger than his own, told the young beaver that this animal was the old master of the pool. This fellow's constant worry was the dam and whatever repairs it needed. He was heading for it now.

Feeling more motion in the water, the young beaver looked around and saw another flat head. It cautiously swam toward him, circling to find his scent on the faint breeze, for a stranger might be dangerous, and sure recognition in the half darkness could best be made through scent.

The young beaver knew when he was recognized, for he saw the other drop all caution and come straight toward him. It was a friendly move. This was one of his sisters; but she took little interest and continued on her way across the pond. Disappointed, he followed her for a few moments then turned back and dove to have a look at his old home, the beaver house. A few strokes with his webbed hind feet brought him to the bottom of the pond at the base of the mound of sticks and mud.

Here was a great tangle of logs and brush that generations of beaver had carried there and woven into the mass that made a solid foundation for the mud-covered house above the surface. Without having to look for it, the beaver found and entered the main underwater entrance through the tangle. Any other kind of animal such as an unfriendly otter would have had a hard time to do this.

The entrance was nothing more than a passage or chute thirteen inches wide which led up to the dome. Still swimming but helping himself along with an occasional push against the sides, he reached the air chamber above the surface. This smelled of beaver and was very dark. He climbed up on a low platform and by careful sniffing made sure that his old mother was not there. She had been short tempered and cross when her new family of four was born that spring, and had driven him out of his home. This really was necessary in order to avoid crowding and to give the youngsters a better chance. He could scent them now in their bed of grass on a raised floor at the further end where he had slept before they came. They heard or scented him and, becoming frightened, crawled about and whimpered unhappily.

Feeling like an unwelcome stranger, the young beaver brushed some of the water drops from his fur, then tried to stretch out on the hard floor and humbly pretend he was comfortably at home again. He could see things dimly now because of the light that filtered through several cracks in the roof. These had been left there to give the room some needed fresh air for breathing and to keep the shredded bark and other bedding material more dry and wholesome.

Tired from his journey, the traveler dozed, but was awakened by the sudden appearance of a big beaver from the water at his very elbow. One look she gave him, then hurried to her latest born, made sure they were all right and turned angrily to chase out the visitor. He wanted her to recognize him, to treat him as a long-lost son. When however she came forward furiously, he held out his little front paws to protect his face and backed away inch by inch until forced to flop into a water hole which was used as an exit in case of danger. Diving, he had to swim fast lest the mother catch up to him and nip his tail. This passage was not as wide as the regular entrance nor as neatly made, and it brought him into the pond at the other side of the house.

Less happy now, he swam about for a minute or two then headed toward a burrow in the shore, not unlike the one he had dug. Here however was more hostility. The master beaver came silently from the dam and hurried to head him off. Plainly this burrow too was tenanted and denied to him.

Aimlessly the young beaver circled the pond. He knew all of the windings of its shore, all of the roadways into the woods, but he no longer felt at home. No one wanted him there, all had turned against him. It had

been that way before he journeyed up Tinker's Creek, but he had forgotten.

He felt cold, tired and miserable. The world, once so rosy, was a hard place after all. Coming at length to the dam he met the cottontail hopping back. She stopped in sudden fear, then leaped past him and hurried into a tunnel through the underbrush on the bank. He was not a meat eater, but the cottontail knew she was trespassing

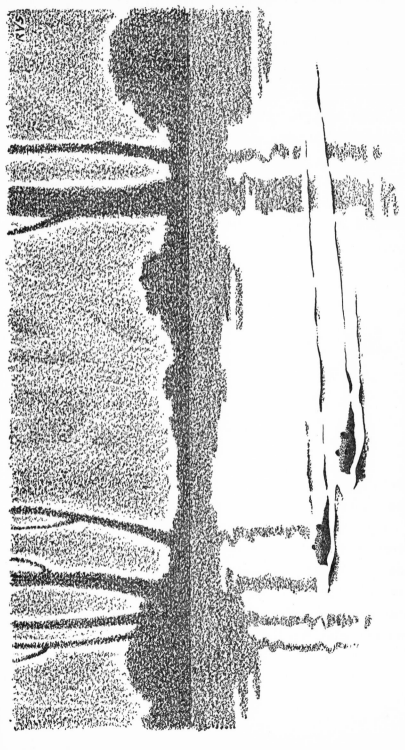

THEY STARTED FOR THE SHORE TO FIND FOOD

and so should take no chances. Dully he climbed out on the mass of sticks and mud.

A soft patter made him look around sharply. From the stream below a beaver was climbing up the bank to reach the pond. Her fur was dry, fluffy and beautiful. She saw him but pretended not to as she crawled over the end of the dam and slipped into the deep water.

The young beaver was alert now, deeply interested. Here was the pretty one whom he had always liked. Into the pond he plunged and swam after her. She dove at once. Wildly searching, he dove too. But she had eluded him, he could find her nowhere. Up to the surface he came to look and listen. The pond was all ripples now from the force of a brisk little breeze. Wavelets looked like heads and heads like wavelets. In vain he hurried around and around. At length he remembered another burrow in the edge of the shore where he and his sister recently had lived and where he had often seen this pretty one. Rushing in that direction he dove and found the entrance. The water carried a pleasing scent; he knew he was on the right track.

A few quick strokes of his powerful hind legs carried him through the passage and up into the beginning of the air chamber. Here was absolute darkness yet he sensed the closeness of another living creature. Slowly and cautiously he advanced until his nose almost touched another nose and he knew that he had found her. Mum-

43

bling and chirping with happiness he tried to touch her, but she kept him at a distance with quick pats from her front feet that were like little hands.

They were very gentle pats, but they made him see that he must keep away. Any other young beaver he would gladly have crowded and perhaps fought just then. But the gentle, pretty one was somehow different from all of the others. There was not much room in the burrow, but she moved about as if exploring her home for the first time, and wherever she went he followed. At last she quietly dove into the water passage and came to the surface of the pond.

Scarcely had her head appeared before his came up beside her. They listened attentively to the sounds of the night, then started for the shore to find food. It was at this moment, in the shadow of the trees on the bank, that a rival male saw the pair.

IV

THE PRETTY ONE

With the bulging ripple in front of the chin that a big beaver pushes before him in swimming fast, the rival bore down upon them. The pretty one only edged to one side with a single stroke from one of her hind feet, but for her companion this was a more serious matter. The young beaver recognized this other fellow and felt afraid, for here was a full grown male, older than he and a real bully. He had never been in a serious fight. He did not know now just what he should do, but the other's evident fury made him suddenly feel an answering rage. He had someone to fight for, and this male did not belong in the pond anyway. Baring his chisel teeth he faced him.

Neither of the two cared to rush in at close quarters.

45

They held each other off with quick thrusts from the front feet and revolved in a circle with nose facing nose, both wrinkled by the most unpleasant sneers that could be produced by such usually peace-loving creatures. When the big fellow suddenly dove the young beaver did likewise, so that they met and buffeted each other under water, then came to the surface in a swirling mass of kicking feet and flapping tails. Little tufts of fur floated around them and spun down wind on the surface of the water.

This might have gone on for a long time, since each fighter was in good condition and unable to tire the other or to hurt him seriously; but the noise of the splashing soon drew another animal to the spot. A red fox with a long, bushy, white tipped tail came running along the bank. Hopefully he looked across the several yards of water to the fighters, expecting them, in their fury, to forget caution. He was not a good enough swimmer to go into the pond after such experts.

Although he blended with the bushes like one of the moving shadows the lady beaver saw him and instinctively knew that he might mean harm, so throwing her tail into the air she brought it flat side down on the water with a smack that could be heard all around the pond. At the same instant she dove, the smack of the tail and the dive being all in one motion. The fighters dove; other beavers around the pond dropped whatever they were

46

A RED FOX CAME RUNNING ALONG THE BANK

doing and dove. In a moment the water seemed deserted.

But in their various bank burrows and in the house on the point the beavers were safely hidden while they waited for the danger to pass. None of them, except the lady beaver who had given the alarm, had any idea of what kind of enemy had appeared; but all had heeded the signal, well knowing that what was dangerous to one might be dangerous to all.

After a few moments of looking about, the fox grew impatient and discouraged. Like the great horned owl he was not at all anxious to tackle a big beaver anyway. Little kitten beavers were his prey. So he slunk away in the direction of the meadows where field mice could be found.

The young beaver in swimming under water had found a burrow, unused and half closed by cave-ins. It ran from near the bottom of the pond up to the very center of the roots around the base of a swamp maple. Above the water level the place smelled of muskrats and was musty, but it seemed safe.

For a quarter of an hour he stayed there listening and waiting and smoothing his fur which the rumpus had made more wet than usual. Then he started down the passage, swam under water to the center of the pond and rose so slowly to the surface that the top of his head appeared above it without a telltale ripple. Now he could look all around and see whether the outside world were again safe for him. There was no sign of his big rival or of any other beaver.

Five minutes of silent watching convinced him that all was well. The black shore line was motionless and quiet, only the water tumbling over the dam made a noise loud enough to really break the stillness. On some days he knew it made no noise at all, but tonight the rain had increased the flow.

He remembered the lady beaver and dove to find her burrow. She was there, somewhere in the darkness. He sensed that, as soon as his head came above the water level; but she was still scared and in no humor to admit visitors to her home. When he came toward her she complained shrilly and finally chased him back into the tunnel. Surprised, he slowly swam away.

Day was beginning to break. Soon the light would be so bright that no animal could swim about the pool without being clearly visible to foe as well as friend.

The young beaver knew that the time had come for him quickly to hide. He could not risk the trip back to Tinker's Pond in daylight nor could he invade the homes of other beaver without unpleasant happenings of some kind, so, only one safe place remained, the musty old burrow under the maple tree; and to this he returned. More even than before, it smelled of muskrats, but he tried not to sniff its odors as he sprawled on the dirt platform and rested his tired body. Much had happened to him in the hours since he left Tinker's Pond.

Now all that he cared about was a quiet sleep; but again and again he was awakened by strange noises, tramping on the ground overhead, barks, shouts, and disturbances, somewhere outside in the water, that made it move up and down in the tunnel beside him. He did not know that three fishermen had come to the pond, bringing with them a spaniel puppy. The men were harmless enough just then, with their thoughts on catching trout; but the noise they made worried the beaver. All day he crouched beside the entrance tunnel in readiness to dive at the first sign that his hiding place was discovered. Gone entirely were the pleasant memories of the old pond.

When, with the approach of darkness, outside sounds had quieted down, he swam out of the tunnel. Already other beaver were moving about, cautiously looking around to make sure that the men really had gone. None of them had ever seen human beings, but they were afraid, scared by the memory of harsh voices and by the heavy scent that hung over the pond.

The young beaver suddenly felt the urge to leave the place and go to his own lonesome but quiet little pool up the creek. First, however, he looked for the pretty lady beaver. She was not in the pond. He swam to the dam. Across it the brown rabbit was again hopping on his way to visit a friend. This time the rabbit and the beaver looked at each other with interest, then resumed their travels.

Nowhere was the pretty one to be found. Almost angrily the young beaver started upstream on his long trip to Tinker's dam that now was his. But where the pond narrowed into the mouth of the creek he had to pass two flat rocks, and on one of these he found her

whom he sought. She was busily drying and smoothing her wonderful fur as if quite unconscious of anyone approaching.

Then looking up quite casually she watched him for an instant, sneezed, and again busied herself with the work as if not in the least interested in anything else. In vain the young beaver swam around her and tried to win her attention. Slowly he moved away, then suddenly turned back and rushed at her. In surprise she half jumped, half fell into the water. After her he came, his teeth gritting against each other as he furiously plunged through the water.

The chase was short; he was very fast and quickly caught her. Chattering with fear, she turned to face him. But when it came to punishing her as he had wanted to, he found he could not do it. Her bright little eyes, looking into his, saw this. Everything changed in an instant. The two touched noses, felt friendly again, swam about and played tag over the sand bars; but always it seemed to be she who coyly ran away.

It was a strange courtship. The shadows danced in the disturbed water, ripples started on their way to the other end of the pond, minnows flashed their silver sides as they sped to deeper water, and still these two raced and frolicked among the reflections of the stars.

Suddenly the young beaver stopped. He had thought of his journey. Quieted and serious now, he started up the creek with the pretty one following. She could see that he had some plan.

But when the water grew too shallow for swimming and he began to climb over rocks, she stopped. It was just the same as if she had said, " I go no further." He came back and tried to coax her. She followed him for a few yards, but became panic stricken as soon as she could no longer see the pool. Back she scurried. This happened several times.

At last he gave it up and started on his way alone, not however without many stops and backward glances toward the spot where he had last seen her between two rocks, half in and half out of the water as if hesitating and uncertain of just what she wanted to do. To her, a trip away from the pond was a new experience.

A big owl hooted loudly in the woods. The pretty one turned and dove, but the young beaver gritted his teeth and continued to climb among the rocks and crawl over the shallow riffles.

V

MEETING ENEMIES

THE young beaver did not travel steadily. The night was clear and therefore dangerous. So he moved guardedly from rock to rock, keeping himself hidden as much as possible, always watching, listening and sniffing. When he heard any unusual sound he crouched quite still and waited, only to find that the animal was a friendly deer or a humble little rabbit. At one of the pools he came across two brown mink playing among the rocks after feeding on trout that they had caught, and at a broad stretch of shallows he met, face to face, the old Tinker Creek raccoon who was an expert at clawing out crayfish from their hiding places under stones and roots in the water.

To have a better look at the beaver, the raccoon stopped the work of feeling about with his long-toed front feet, and shook the water from his heavy fur. He cocked his ears forward as his sharp nose explored the scent currents of the air. The old fellow knew that beaver usually lived in ponds and that this one would be away from his home only because of some very good reason. With his mind on food, he left the shallows and inquisitively followed the other animal at a polite distance, hoping that the flat-tailed one might have found, up the stream, something especially good to eat that he could share.

The strange pair traveled this way for nearly an hour, the reddish brown one always in the lead, while the dark brown coon with his round, furry, black-ringed tail continued to keep within watching distance. Twice the beaver stopped to gnaw fresh bark with his rodent teeth, shaped like those of a squirrel. Each time, after he had passed on, the coon hopefully examined these places and was disgusted to find nothing suitable for himself. His set of teeth, a typical meat eater's, placed like those of a cat or dog, could not properly gnaw bark even if he had wanted to dine on such simple fare. The beaver passed by a dead chub which the coon seized at once and ate with relish after first washing each piece of the fish with his usual care.

On sandy bars at the head of little pools the beaver stopped to leave his mark, a dab of mud with his scent. Any male beaver traveling in the spring or summer would have done the same thing, and all other beaver finding one of these dabs would study it and learn about the one who left it. Water could carry away all scent or sign, but the mud dabs on the bars would stay there until the next heavy rain reached them.

The beaver was thinking of his own little pond and the new burrow, not far ahead now. He recognized many of the rocks and pools he passed, and knew that at any moment he might come within sight of the big beams above his home. He hurried now and in his excitement dropped all caution.

Ah, there were the beams. But the pond and his little dam! Both were gone. Slowly now he crawled closer. The dam was broken, swept away in the middle. A peculiar scent hung over the place and startled him; it was strong enough to come from a large animal and it signalled danger.

A black hulk was moving along the bank, followed by two smaller ones. To the beaver, the one in the lead looked enormous, but it was just a good-sized mother bear. The two cubs were skinny little fellows no larger than foxes.

The mother stepped into the water, sloshed about with her front feet and tore out some more of the dam material. She was hunting for frogs, crayfish or anything else edible. Meanwhile the two cubs stayed on the bank and watched. Presently one of them playfully cuffed the other's ear and received a resounding whack in return. Instantly they were rolling about, locked in each other's arms and biting, clawing and growling for all they were worth. Before the mother took the childish squabble seriously, they rolled into the water and got a good fright. The creek was not deep enough to soak them very much, but they took the wetting seriously and scrambled up the bank to a high and dry place where they could lick the drops out of their black fur.

RVS

The scene could have amused an owl or a flying squirrel, safe up in a tree with branches too slim to carry a bear's weight, but to the beaver whose feet were not made for climbing nor for fast running, it was terrifying. He turned and crawled cautiously downstream to a deep little pool beside a ledge of rock. Even the coon, who could climb as well as fight, hurried into the forest, for he knew that a hungry mother bear might try almost anything.

The mother, always sniffing, soon caught the beaver's scent. She threw up her head and searched the stream bed with her little eyes. Seeing nothing move while she watched for nearly a minute, she came striding downstream.

Suddenly she found where the cautious animal had stopped and turned back. It was easy to follow the tracks before the scent had drifted away. Stepping almost noiselessly on her well-padded soles she drew close to the pool.

The beaver, who had been waiting almost breathlessly, sank out of sight entirely and dove into the deepest spot, where he stayed, holding his breath.

The bear reached the pool and looked it over suspiciously. It smelled of beaver. But to make sure, she circled it and found only the scented trails leading to it from both directions. With the cubs now crouching nearby where they could watch all that was going on, she stepped into the water and began to feel about with her front feet, first one, then the other, very much as the coon had done when hunting for crayfish. She knew only too well that the beaver must be hiding in the pool. Through and around it she walked, with the water now up to her

59

breast, now almost to her chin as the depths changed. The little cubs, seeing that things were going to happen, hugged each other in their excitement.

At first the beaver could see the bear and easily dodge her big paws in the deep water, but when the mud became stirred up and the water cloudy, he had only his keen ears and the motion of the water to help him. The bear too knew this and became even more stealthy in her hunting. Once her claws brushed against the beaver's back as he dashed out of reach. Again and again she saw the swirl that his webbed hind feet made in the water as he swam about. These signs kept up the bear's hopes and spurred her on. At times she went entirely under water herself as she searched and wallowed about.

The cubs were dancing around the rim of the pool, regardless of splashes and wet feet. They had never seen a beaver, but they knew that their mother was after some lively kind of creature that would mean food for them. Now on their hind legs, now bumping together and climbing over each other or fighting jealously they pranced and raced around.

This could not last very long. Had the beaver been supplied with gills like those of a fish, all might have been well, but since he had lungs he needed air; every eight or nine minutes his nose had to be stuck out of water. The bear watched for these breathing spells and threw herself at the flat brown head whenever it appeared. And the more he chased about, the more fresh air the beaver needed to keep him going.

He became so breathless that even the cubs heard his gasps and spotted him whenever he came to the surface. More excited than ever they ran around the pool, whining and growling and fighting when they got in each other's way.

No, this could not last. The big bear had the upper hand. Standing in the center of the pool, her black and brown head dripping and her mouth wide open as she panted from the effort of dashing around in the water, she was a grim sight.

The beaver came to the surface behind her, drew in a long breath and dove just as she turned quickly with upraised paws. He swam under water to the other side of the pool, crawled up the side to the very edge and again stuck out his nose and eyes. The bear, still standing on her hind legs, was looking in the other direction.

A new idea came to the beaver. He pulled himself out of the water and crouched among the rocks. Then the bear spun around and looked in his direction. She had heard a slight sound, the click of one pebble against another.

With heaving sides and wildly beating heart, the beaver waited. The bear's eyes seemed fastened on him; she came down on all fours and swung toward him. He knew he could not turn and dash into the pool fast enough to escape; he knew too that in a few great leaps the other animal might overtake him on the land. So he lay there. And still the bear came on.

The night things hemming in the pool seemed absolutely still. The trees, the big rock at one side and the shadows in the forest. Only the black hulk in the water disturbed the quiet scene as she moved ever nearer, sending little shivers of reflected starlight along the surface.

The beaver's leg muscles were already tightening for the leap that had to come, his toe nails dug into the sand. And then came a yowl, almost a shriek. One of the cubs had playfully clawed the other, really hurting him and making the little fellow as mad as a hornet. A furious tussle commenced. The mother looked around angrily. She started toward the youngsters who promptly broke apart and began a wild chase around the pool.

The beaver's muscles relaxed, he breathed again. But right over his back came the cubs as if he were a stone. When however first one and then the other struck soft, yielding fur, they knew something was wrong. Forgotten was the quarrel as they turned around to see what this strange soft lump could be.

One reached forward gingerly and touched it with his paw. This was too much for the beaver. He suddenly jumped up, scaring the cubs so badly that they nearly fell over backwards. Then he ran. And because he seemed afraid of them, the cubs got back their nerve and ran after him.

The old bear glimpsed only what looked like another race between the cubs; but a moment later she saw everything more clearly. They were chasing another animal, the beaver! With two great splashing leaps she came out of the pool and dashed after them. Stones flew as she scrambled along the stream bed.

The beaver was heading for his burrow, running for his life. Behind came the bears in a pack, clattering,

splashing and crashing. Just as the entrance to the burrow showed ahead, the mother passed the cubs and made a mighty jump that landed her almost on top of her quarry. Her claws tried to grip him. She struck fast and furiously like a cat at a mouse, but missed, and the beaver reached the hole, going in headlong regardless of bumps and dirt.

At the last instant down came the bear's left paw on his tail, pinning him with one sharp claw. He struggled forward, bracing himself against the sides of the burrow and pulling with every ounce of muscle in his strong body. It hurt him. The pain shot all the way up his spine as he strained; and suddenly he felt dizzy and weak. Then the tail ripped! The claw cut through the end and lost its hold. He was free! Slowly he dragged himself further into the burrow while behind him he heard the bear snorting with disappointment and tearing at the earth with claws and teeth.

VI

SURPRISES

THE old bear dug and ripped the soft earth until she encountered a heavy stone. Against this her claws could do nothing, so she tried digging around it. Once more she made headway, but suddenly cut loose a cluster of tree roots which had helped to hold up the sloping bank. At once a deluge of earth and stone came rushing down on top of her and blocked the hole already dug. Sneezing and panting, she backed out and sat down to rest and look at the damage.

There was no fun in trying to dig away a young hill, so with a good shake to get the earth out of her black fur, she gave it up and turned aside to take a drink. While she lay sprawled beside the water, cleaning out her mouth and licking her paws, the nimble cubs played at sliding down the bank. They could see that their mother was feeling cross and should be left alone. Soon, however, they found her in better humor and willing to feed them from her breast. Greedily they helped themselves and thereafter thought no more of hunting the beaver.

When meal time was past, all three went wandering down the stream bed though, unlike the beaver, they kept out of the water as much as they could.

Back in his burrow, in total blackness, the beaver had crouched waiting for whatever might happen. But when the noise of digging and scraping came no nearer and finally ended, he grew bold enough to crawl forward for a look at things. No light showed at the entrance. All sounds of the bear had died away, so, after listening a little while longer, he began to work at the mass of earth that blocked the way to light and food.

It was not like digging in from the outside where there was plenty of room to throw the dirt. In the cramped tunnel he soon had no place to put any more of it and was blocked in on all sides. A new fear gripped him there, in the tight, hot darkness among the masses of earth that let in so little air to breathe. A few more quick strokes against the wall in front and he had filled up the last open space. The earth was jamming even his body against the side of the burrow and clogging the sweep of his paws. It was almost as if he were tied down and choked.

When he could dig no more, he lay still and rested, then jumped at the task again with renewed strength. His courage had come back and he was determined to get out. More earth was packed away, jammed hard around him. Another rest, longer this time. Now he dug with only one paw, the others being stuck fast. Scratch went his claws; he had hit a firm stone. No use to work against this, it could not be budged.

The beaver placed his hot nose against the coolness of the stone and lay still. Around him there was no sound; he was buried alive and there was no one to help. Every few minutes he fought against the earth or pressed his head harder on the stone, but all his pent-up strength could make no impression now, and the muscles that had grown for two years until they fairly bulged beneath his soft fur seemed weak and useless.

The air grew more stifling; it made him drowsy. He closed his heavy eyelids and dozed.

Then came a great clatter. Outside, the bear, returning upstream with her cubs, had stopped to take a look at the burrow. She leaped on top of the pile of new earth, sniffed here and there, turned over a stone or two and hopefully dug out a few big paw loads of dirt. Loose stones rolled or slid into the rocky stream bed and annoyed her with the noise. Now that the light of day had come, she feared her enemy, man, and the possibility that he might hear the racket and steal up there to hurt her or her cubs. Also, she was too impatient to dig for long. A few more strong scoops with her paw and she hit another big stone. That settled it; she would dig no more. Away she strode, with the tired cubs following her heels and whining to make her go more slowly.

But behind this big stone, scarcely further from her than the length of her nose, had lain the beaver wide awake again but absolutely still except for his thumping heart. He had plainly heard the bear's every move and expected her to find him. Her last sniff had sounded very close, and the stone had stirred when she struck it.

As soon as he dared, he tried again to fight the earth. This time something moved, he felt less cramped. Another fierce shove brought more headroom, and a third effort pushed the stone at least an inch. Fresh air poured in; there was a flood of light from above and the stone leaned outwards.

He knew he was free. Slowly, carefully he crawled out of the hole, then sprawled on his stomach and rested. Vireos were singing and a crow cawed.

Presently he felt strong enough to go to the water and wallow in its coolness. The crow stopped its cawing and flew closer to have a good look at such an unusual sight as this in broad daylight. He thought that his mate should see it also and called to her; whereupon she came

RVS

AWAY SHE STRODE, WITH THE TIRED CUBS FOLLOWING

and perched near him on a convenient limb. The beaver still wallowed and washed his face without more than a glance at the two birds. He blinked at the sun and its reflection in the water.

But the bear might return, also the water made his tail smart where the bear's claws had ripped it. So out he crawled and walked back to the burrow.

After a look all around he entered its mouth and commenced to dig out the dirt that had held him prisoner; and this time he made it fairly fly. In a short time the passage was open. The entrance, once so well hidden, now was spoiled, and the weeds all tramped down by the bears, but it was the only hiding place he could safely reach. So he went inside and threw himself down, to sleep as soundly as if nothing unusual had happened in a long time. He did not stir, indeed, until the deep shadows came and the little bats began to circle over the dam, dipping and dodging as they chased the new crop of flying insects. Somewhere in the woods a whippoorwill was uttering his loud call again and again. Once more all seemed well with the world.

So the beaver, after stretching his legs a few times, came out of his burrow for a good look around, sniffed the fragrance of the woods, and ambled hurriedly, but still rather stiffly, upstream to the bank where maple shoots and willows could be found. He gnawed fast and carried some of the shoots down to the water to be nibbled or debarked there at his leisure. Then, moved by the hope of finding a safer place than the burrow, he traveled upstream on an exploring expedition.

Nowhere could he find a spot nearly as good for a dam as the one he had left. Upstream there were wider banks, fine for a pond but requiring too much work for him to tackle alone. Therefore, before the moon set he journeyed back to his burrow. But in front of it crouched a brown animal that seemed to be lying in wait for him. Quickly he sank into the shallow water until only the top of his head showed.

He saw the other animal begin to move about. It went to the mouth of the burrow, then down to the water's edge, then back again to the burrow. It looked now no larger than himself, and suddenly he began to notice something familiar about it.

Surely this was no dangerous enemy. At last he caught the scent and leaped out of the stream with excitement. Instantly the other creature took fright and rushed into the burrow—his burrow—just as if the stranger belonged there. And when he scrambled after it and met at the entrance the soft face and bright eyes of his friend, the pretty little lady beaver from the pond below, he knew that this stranger did belong there and must never be made to leave. Whining a greeting he tried to lick her pointed nose and then rushed around in circles like one gone mad with joy.

SURPRISES

She had left her pond, urged by loneliness and an instinct that she did not understand, and had slowly and coyly followed his trail all of the way up Tinker's Creek. Two beavers now watched the silly antics of the little bats; a new era had indeed begun for Tinker's good old dam!

VII

THE WOODS FOLK

It rained lightly through all of the following day. The two beavers did not care, nor, indeed, did any of the well feathered, or well furred woods folk. The natural oiliness of their covering, aided by the perfect arrangement of every feather and every hair to shed water, saved their bodies from a wetting. From time to time the birds needed a little extra waterproof dressing from the oil sack each carried on his back near the base of the tail, and the animals required a minute or two of careful licking or combing of their fur to keep that in shape; but light rain did not really worry them.

They went about their daily work, some finding it easier on account of the wet weather, others finding it a little harder. The robins and crows had no difficulty in securing all the worms they wanted to eat, these slimy crawlers finding the moisture exactly to their liking and therefore coming to the surface of the ground to get as much as possible of its benefits.

The grouse, quail and other birds that liked to scratch for a living found it hard to move the soggy, dead leaves. Among these birds there was one exception, the great wild gobbler who lived nearly all year on the wooded ridge that formed the left bank of Tinker's Creek. His powerful red legs could make wet or dry leaves fly in all directions. Loudly he gobbled in the misty, half light of the early morning, then finding no friendly reply from his mate who was hidden from him on her nest of four brown-speckled eggs, he strutted about, just as if he did not care, and, suddenly remembering his hunger, trotted to the base of a big oak where he scratched the ground like any old rooster, hunting for acorns that had fallen during the autumn before and, because they did not land in the right kind of moist ground, had not yet sprouted.

The gobbler was a gorgeous bird and he knew it. Even in the rain his dark feathers shimmered and shone, while his wet neck wattles gleamed bright red.

Suddenly he " froze," ceased all moving as if he had been turned into rock or wood. And now that there was no movement to catch the eye he looked like a black stump, so much so indeed that he fooled the Tinker's

Creek bobcat who at that moment came sneaking around a clump of bushes.

The bobcat, however, saw the newly turned leaves under the oak and went closer to investigate. Almost under his nose the black stump turned into a wild turkey and leaped into the air with a great crash and swish of wings, scaring the cat and escaping without a scratch. Down into the valley soared the grand bird; but in the line of his flight instantly galloped the hungry bobcat.

As soon as he was out of sight of the enemy the gobbler felt safe and looked for a good place in which to alight. Soaring more and more slowly on set wings he landed in the creek bed not far from the beaver's burrow. Here, on a dry gravel bar, he strutted and gobbled in fine good humor over his easy escape.

The cat was then loping down the ridge; but at the first gobble he stopped and listened so attentively that, when the turkey gobbled once more, the keen hunter marked the exact spot where the sound came from. Again he loped forward, then slowed down to a cautious crawl, and no creature in the woods could outcrawl him.

When he came to the old beams that marked the former dam he stretched his neck to peep over them and saw not only the big gobbler but also the young beaver who, awakened by the gobbler and knowing that a wary bird like the turkey would not be making such a noise if

76

UP FLEW THE GOBBLER AND AWAY DASHED THE BEAVER

he thought any enemy were near, had slipped out for a drink and a look around.

One glimpse of the bobcat would have scared the gobbler, but the innocent look of a beaver shuffling out of his burrow was a different matter, and only interested him. And so it happened that while death in the form of the hungry cat was moving down the bank a few inches at a time the old bird and the flat-tailed animal were looking at each other with interest, and thinking of nothing else.

The beaver was between the gobbler and the cat, very near now. So it was on his shoulders that the yellow eyes were focused as they came nearer.

Only one other creature saw the bobcat; the crow, who had a liking for this part of the old dam bed, came flying down the valley just in time to glimpse the tufted ears and switching bob tail of the spotted killer.

" Caw'r'r'r'r," he cried at the top of his voice.

Such a warning could not be mistaken. The gobbler crouched for a leap into the air, and the beaver tensed his muscles for a rush to safety. Both of them looked in all directions.

" Caw'r'r'r'r! Caw'r'r'r'r! " again screamed the crow, now hovering directly over the cat and thus showing the exact location of the enemy of the woods folk. " Caw'r'r'r'r! "

Up flew the gobbler and away dashed the beaver. But the cat sprang. Directly over the bushes and down the

79

bank in a beautiful dive that should have landed all four clawed feet on top of the poor flat-tail.

Stones flew as the beaver scuttled wildly for the burrow. The cat was over him, legs outspread, claws extended, mouth open in a vicious grin. But it could not check its body or turn around in the air and so overshot its mark. Had the burrow been anywhere but under the bank, and had the beaver been running in any direction except toward the cat, there would have been a different

ending. Before the spotted acrobat could land and turn around, the beaver had reached the entrance.

How the crow enjoyed all of this show! Safe overhead on his black wings, he circled the scene and scolded. The more the cat glared, the more he cawed with joy and triumph, calling his mate, his children and his friends to come quickly and see the fun.

THE WOODS FOLK

And they came! A dozen of them, each adding his caws to the general clamor until the woods re-echoed with the din.

Suddenly the cat leaped wickedly at them, striking up as high as its claws could go. But the crows only dodged and mocked. They seemed almost to brush the tufted ears with their wing tips as they hovered and circled, or dipped and shot upwards again.

Suddenly the cat sneaked away and soon was hidden by the bushes, but the excited birds cawed and circled until they were certain that the show was really all over. Then, one by one, they flew away to finish the more serious matter of finding their morning meal.

The beavers remained hidden. They dared not leave the burrow. All day they watched the entrance and worried lest some new enemy find them and force his way into the unprotected entrance. Both knew that water must, somehow, be made to hide their home.

Scarcely had the sun set when first the male and then his companion crept out, nibbled the bark of a few twigs along the stream and then at once began to cut and carry long branches from the alder bushes. These they stacked in the exact place where the young beaver had previously begun his dam.

Sods, wet and slippery by the time they had been ferried across the pool, were solidly poked into place by the expert front paws. With good material close at hand the work soon was showing results. However, when the gaps in the new structure were only half sealed the beavers grew weary and stopped operations for the night. Before hiding in the burrow, as day approached, they wandered about their slim line of brush and mud, gloating over the way it already seemed to slow up the flow of the stream.

VIII

BUILDING A DAM

A NORTHWEST wind followed the rain, chasing away all clouds and bringing much cooler weather. The beavers were disturbed by the change; they felt more restless. In addition to their other perils came with this new chill in the air the forecast of bitter winter, when ice would form on the streams and snow would cover the woods. They had seen what winter could do to soft, friendly waters.

Through all the hours of darkness they worked on the dam, each cutting branches and lugging them, one at a time, to be anchored in whatever seemed the best place along the slowly growing line. Usually alders were chosen. They were tough, light and in great clumps along the edge of the stream. Some of the stems, where the beavers' teeth gnawed them, were as thick as a man's arm.

When sods that could easily be dug up seemed hard to find anywhere near at hand, the beavers used stones for strengthening the dam, rolling, shoving and pulling the larger ones along the bottom of the stream until they could be jammed into the odd-looking structure. Sometimes they tried to move stones larger than themselves, but soon found this too difficult, although they pushed with all their might, using head, chest and shoulder against the object.

And the water gradually rose behind the dam! It became a very healthy looking pond with little waves all its own when blasts of wind struck down from the peaks. Along its sides stuck up the tops of the trees and taller bushes from the flooded ground. The tired beavers now not only swam to their burrow but also had to dive to find it.

Night after night they continued to work, always, however, finding it a little harder to anchor and plaster down the limbs as the height and length of the dam increased. The water had a way of crawling around the ends as fast as leaks were found and repaired. But after the second week they had run the ends out far enough to stop this. Now they went all over the dam, adding load after load of mud and roots to strengthen everything.

The length was about thirty-four feet, and the height more than three, while the width, judged by the long alder brush, looked six or seven feet; the mud filling,

NOW THEY WENT ALL OVER THE DAM. TO STRENGTHEN EVERYTHING

however, made merely a narrow strip along the side nearest the pond.

But work was far from being ended. Now the burrow, which never had been intended for anything more than a temporary shelter, seemed gloomy, damp and unsatisfactory for winter use, so the young beaver ran an entirely new tunnel up from the bottom of the pond into a little point of land on which grew alders that he had left there for the special purpose of holding and protecting a house. On top of this sharp little point the two home makers now heaped brush, logs, mud and roots so that the tunnel could come up to the surface of the ground and into this mass of tangled material without exposing the beavers. The interior of the mass was hollowed out to make a living room, and when the material had been heaped nearly four feet high, the inside chamber was roomy enough for a landing platform and for a sleeping floor, just as in the house the young beavers had left. There was also a second entrance or exit tunnel in case of danger.

At first, grass was carried in to make a bed, but both beavers knew how soft and clean cedar bark and shreds of the wood would be, so they searched along the creek and up into the high ground until they actually found a stout red cedar and cut it down. The branches were trimmed off and the trunk cut into two foot logs that could be pulled to the water and then ferried into the house where narrow strips were pulled off and chewed and shredded until they made a big heap of soft, wonderful bedding that would not get soggy with the dampness nor harbor little insects which like lice were carried from place to place in the beavers' fur.

Still there was more work to be done. Winter was closing in and there was no food stored under water where ice would not wall it off from the beavers. So several nights were spent in cutting down cottonwoods, maples and birches, lopping off the branches, dividing the trunks into whatever lengths their thickness made advisable for easy carriage and anchoring all of this wood in the water beside the house. It was an enormous amount of labor. Soon this tangled woodpile became well water soaked and heavier. It settled down into the water as far as the mud bottom where the coldest winter could not be expected to touch the lower branches with ice.

Snow came and skim ice. Feverishly the two animals carried fresh, soft mud onto the house to form a roof coating that would freeze almost as hard as stone and keep out the cold as well as enemies. At the middle of the top, however, they left a few cracks unplastered to serve as a ventilator.

A last careful coating of mud on the dam and a few repairs completed the urgent work. Now winter might come in earnest, the beavers were ready for it.

BUILDING A DAM

And come it did. The ice covered the pond, snow filled the woods. Up the stream there was an opening where the water was swift and a small spring that trickled out of the bank, warm enough to keep away some of the ice. Through this hole the beavers sometimes came out at night to get some more wood and to look at the changed world around them. The muskrats used it also, when the mink were not around, and they were small enough to be

able to tunnel galleries under the protecting surface of the snow to reach their favorite kinds of roots in the bank.

The key to the beavers' comfort and safety was the dam that held in the water of the deep little pond. They watched this with great care. It was new and just a little weak in places, but it did not leak very much. Indeed, considering the speed with which it was put together, it was a great success.

CHISEL-TOOTH, THE BEAVER

Inside the snow-covered house or lodge the two beavers rested after their great labors and listened to the ice crack and the wind whistle around the frozen woods. At each meal time they dived into the water tunnel, pulled a short branch or a log out of the woodpile and brought it up the tunnel and into the dark little room where the tasty inner layer of bark could be gnawed off by the front chisel teeth and chewed by the big grinders in the back

RVS

of the mouth. The branch, stripped white, was then pulled down the tunnel and discarded unless it was needed for the dam.

Twice, during the winter, warm spells thawed most of the ice. Then more water rushed down the creek and put a great strain on the dam. It was then that the beavers decided for safety to build a second or supporting dam a few yards below. They began this work but could not complete it at once.

In February the two muskrats that lived in a bank burrow they had dug in the edge of the pond, were so scared by their enemies, the mink, that they took refuge in the beaver lodge. First one, then the other came in rather sheepishly, as if expecting to be driven out. But the good-natured beavers made no fuss, and the humble rats, whose fur was warm but less beautiful than that of their new friends, hollowed out a little room for themselves in the side of the house. They quarrelled occasionally and were restless neighbors, but otherwise did not interfere. Sometimes they nibbled a twig which they took from the woodpile, but there was in storage plenty for all; and so passed the winter.

IX

A FAMILY

Spring approached slowly, then gained strength with a rush and suddenly burst open the old, rotten ice blanket on the pond. The melting snow and warm rains flooded the creek, the water seethed and roared. It poured over the dam in a mass many inches deep.

The beavers watched the water with misgivings. It rose in their house and covered the landing floor, it crept up to the bed platform and wet the shredded cedar. Now something had to be done. Without any panic the beavers began to gnaw and work at their ceiling, making it higher, and packing the ceiling material on the sleeping platform to raise it above the water. But still the water rose. Then the young beaver made up his mind to do a dangerous thing. He swam out of the water tunnel and examined the flooded dam. At its weakest place he began to tear it apart, frantically gnawing and digging a break in its top. His mate came to help.

Once the rushing water which threatened the whole structure swept them off their feet and carried them over the dam, but they were unhurt and returned to the work, tearing and pulling until the creek found a way into this new hole and raced through it, carrying away a few more sticks and much mud, but leaving the remainder of the dam unspoiled.

At once the water level was lowered, the pressure on the dam relieved. Morning came and the tired beavers returned to their house. For three days the flood continued. By that time the rain had ceased and the snow been carried away from a large part of the mountains. The creek no longer roared.

Then, after a look at the dam the beavers went to work repairing it. They filled in the big hole with the wood they had peeled during the winter, they jammed new sods into the crevices and piled brush on top until it was stronger than ever.

Now, with the creek still too full to be forded easily, the dam was used as a bridge by many land animals. Foxes trotted over it; rabbits, skunks and even the brown weasels profited by it. The little animal world was on the move, the great spring mating time was at hand. The woods were free from the solid grip of the deep snow, food was again plentiful.

What remained of the beavers' woodpile was deserted. Fresher, more tasty bark could be found in the woods, the sweet sap was running in the sugar maples. The beavers ate their fill and frolicked around the pond in the full knowledge that winter was past and summer ahead.

One day in April the young beaver's mate grew short tempered. She nagged at him and finally made him leave the lodge. Disturbed and not understanding this at all, he swam to the old burrow under the rotten timbers and moped there alone. When on the next night he returned to the lodge he heard strange whimperings and found in the nest two little creatures that he had never before seen. They were just like himself but lighter in color and helplessly squirmy. He looked at them and backed away.

Less than a month after that he saw the two young beavers swimming around the lodge with their mother. They were playful youngsters always ready to roll about on the logs and chase each other around the woodpile. On clear days they sunned themselves on the side of the lodge that sloped toward the deepest water. Even at that age they were always ready, at the shadow of a hawk, or the alarm call and splash of the mother, to dash into the water and hide.

Soon they learned to go ashore and eat tender shoots

of the growing things. From the beginning they had known how to swim, now they learned how to run along the paths that their parents had made into the woods to reach the best birch trees. On the warmer nights they played all around the pond, guarded by the watchful eyes of both parents, for now their father was taking more interest in the pair.

The first almost fatal accident came in the middle of May. It was in the early evening. The mother beaver was watching at the edge of the pond while the young-

sters dug luscious roots in the bank. Suddenly she saw, above some long grass, the tufted ears and round yellow eyes of the Tinker's Creek bobcat. Slap went her flat tail on the water with such a noise that it scared the cat as well as warning the young beavers. They scurried for the water, but so hurriedly that for a few seconds one became tangled in the grass. That was all the cat needed. Recovered from the shock of the noise he plunged after this unfortunate youngster.

CHISEL-TOOTH, THE BEAVER

Terror made the little fellow almost numb, but he rallied and rolled the remainder of the way down the bank and into the water with the cat barely missing him in its last spring. In the pond the youngster was safe. How he loved the friendly water! The cat could prowl around all it wanted to without again finding a beaver ashore after that.

One danger, however, lurked in the water. That

spring an otter came wandering up Tinker's Creek. He was a big, brown fellow, with glossy, straw-colored coat over the neck and shoulders. When he reached the pond he knew from the fresh scent on the dam that beavers were somewhere nearby, young beavers too; but his first thought was a fish for a meal. During his night's journey he had found none in the more shallow waters.

And so the otter dived and explored along the bottom

of the pond, looking for a flash of silver or the red brown sides of a trout. Around and around he went and still around, searching the bank edges, the deep places and the shallows at the far upper end. Young fish there were in plenty, but none large enough for him. At length he sprang up on the dam, disappointed and in bad humor.

Then he saw the beaver family. Rearing up to get a better view he watched them enter the water from a path in the woods. First came the watchful mother, then the two young, and last of all the father, for he was lugging a branch. Otter scent hung over the pond just enough to be a warning. With a little scream of fear to the young the mother dived and the youngsters dived too. They headed under water for the lodge, and the otter could not see them then. In the water's edge the father lay quite still, looking for the danger. A tail slap would have made him dive too, but the call might mean only the need for precaution. He saw the long body of the otter slide noiselessly into the water and then knew how serious was the situation.

The slap of his tail as he dived alarmed all of the nearby woods folk. But instead of heading for the lodge and leading the enemy to the nest he dashed for the burrow and won the entrance just as the otter came shooting after his flat black tail. Inside, he gained the air chamber and then whirled around.

In a moment the otter's flat head came up in front of

him. Neither could see the other in the dark, but their noses were active and the enemy caught the scent of a full grown angry male beaver close at hand and ready and willing to fight. There was no fear in that scent!

The otter hesitated. Fierce as he was he did not relish a fight with a sixty-pound tough old male armed with chisel teeth. There was no scent of the kitten beavers. There in the dark he showed his own sharp teeth in a wicked sneer, then backed, turned and hurried out of the tunnel to hunt the kittens elsewhere. After a minute or two the father beaver followed him.

It was not long before the otter found the old wood-pile in front of the lodge. He circled it twice, boring in here and there, searching. Then he saw the main entrance to the house. Slowly, cautiously he pushed his way up.

The beavers in the chamber above heard him coming, the young cowered in the back of the nest, the mother came slightly forward, her teeth gritting together. Up came the otter's head. He drew a long breath, at the same time scenting the kittens. Up came his long, powerful neck.

The mother's sudden cry sent the young scuttling for the danger tunnel at the other end. They made a noise in their scrambling and the otter, still unable to see them, charged. He struck the mother with his shoulder and checked himself at the sound of her teeth. She

THE OTTER SWAYED THIS WAY AND THAT

backed away and took a defensive position with her back against the wall. The otter swayed this way and that, sniffing, trying to see. The scent now told him that the young had somehow gone.

With a chirp of rage he turned and dived. Outside in the pond he hunted the fugitives. The wiser young one, he who had so nearly been caught by the cat, had dashed for the burrow, the other, bewildered by fright, had hidden in some brush near the bank. This one the otter found.

But the youngster was quick and scrambled up on the shore, hiding again in the thick tangles of the bushes. And as luck would have it, at that moment the bobcat came prowling along and met the excited otter face to face. Both crouched. Each knew that the other was a formidable adversary, but only the otter knew that a kitten beaver was helplessly close. He tried to outglare the cat, but the latter's yellow eyes never left his and the

tufted ears turned back as the ominous cat growl rum-
bled out of the spotted throat. He had been master of
Tinker's Creek; no otter, however big, could out-face
him.

As long as the safety of the water remained so close,
the otter dared at first to be nasty in return, but his nerve
gave way and he backed off. Big beavers and bobcats
wherever he went! And no eatable fish. It was no place
for him. With another chirp he breasted the pond and,
restless wanderer that he was, he went straight for the
lower waters of the creek, never to return.

But the bobcat had an idea. Something must have
lured the otter to the shore. Carefully he searched the
bushes, almost stepping on the hidden kitten beaver
which leaped up and made a rush for the water. The
bushes were very thick and kept the big cat from a fatal
spring. A splash and the little beaver was in the pond.
Slap came down the mother's tail on the water near the
lodge. She had seen the chase. Slap sounded the father's alarm signal. The cat glared and skulked back to
the higher woods. The ripples died away on the pond
and all was quiet.

DANGER

Autumn once more chilled the air. Wild ducks which in flying overhead had discovered the pond, fed in a flock at the lower end. Two great blue herons stalked the shallows for minnows, and at night were joined by several small black crowned night herons whose harsh but friendly cry of " quawk " filled the woods when they flew from their day roosts in the highest oaks.

These did not disturb the beavers. Again it was work time and there was much to be done. Already the small supporting dam had been built up below the first one. More strength had been given to the main dam by the addition of new brush and plenty of root-filled mud. Nearly a foot had been added to the height, and the same amount to the lodge. Also, since the cottonwoods grew a hundred yards from the pond's edge, the beavers had begun a little canal to take the place of the temporary road they had made and used in pulling logs to the water.

The canal was difficult to keep full of water at the upper end, so the father beaver had run a smaller canal or sluiceway to a spring which previously had flowed into the creek below the dam but now was made to feed the canal. Several little dams across the canal kept the water about a foot deep along its whole length, in spite of the slope. As the floating wood had to be pulled over these dams they slowed up the log hauling, but were necessary unless the canal were made very much deeper where the slope rose upwards.

The youngsters, still small, helped as much as their strength allowed and wrestled with the logs which their parents cut. They even tried, with might and main, to fell the trees, but the cuts their little teeth made in trunks eight inches thick were so puny that their parents always helped them. Besides that, felling trees was dangerous work unless one knew by experience in which direction a cut tree would fall. Every night the loud sound of chisel teeth tearing big chips out of wood could be heard around the pond, and this year the winter supply of hard wood with its nourishing bark was stored up before the first real freeze. Gone was the fear of winter, the pond now supported a prosperous, happy family.

First ice, then snow. Everywhere whiteness. In the sunlight the mountains shimmered against the blue of the sky, and between them lay the little pond, frozen in, apparently uninhabited. Yet, looking closely, one could see a wisp of steam, heated air, rising gently from the top of a little mound on a point of land. Inside that little mound were the four beavers, always busy at something, even if it was only at drying or combing their soft fur

after a watery trip to the log pile. And with them, in their own little separate room, still were the two muskrats. Water lovers all and beautifully protected against the cold, they cared not if the wind blew from the north or the water became the temperature of liquid ice.

And so winter passed. Once more the father was driven from the lodge and once more the whimpering of little beavers greeted him when he came to have a look at the cosy lodge. But now there were four in the big new bed built by the mother, while the two half grown youngsters of last year slept at one side. And for the new family the lodge had to be enlarged; the muskrats, their humble little space being needed, had to go.

Fortunately, the rats could still go to their own burrow. They, too, soon had a family of little ones to care

for, and here also the father was made to leave and to live like a bachelor somewhere else.

All of this time man had overlooked Tinker's little creek. No wonder the wild creatures throve and grew unsuspicious in their security. The gentle deer walked in the cooling water during any hour of the day, gray squirrels barked at each other, fearless of noise. The turkeys stalked across the dam, grouse drummed in the bushes; fat bullfrogs sat on the pond edge and boomed whenever they felt like it. Then, on the most beautiful quiet day of early summer, came Whitey Flynn. A hunter and trapper by nature, he, like the Tinker's Creek bobcat, was making a tour of investigation to see what he could find of any use to him.

Stealthily he sneaked along the stream until suddenly his pale face with its rim of white hair was thrust through the wall of greenery which screened the beaver pond. A soft whistle of surprise escaped his lips. He grinned happily as his roving eyes caught everywhere the sure signs that this new pond was inhabited by a large family of beavers.

Cautiously he walked to the main dam, noted the perfection of the work, the enormous amount of labor all of this building of dams, lodge, canals, roads and woodpile must represent. But his admiration was not really stirred. He was, indeed, only trying to translate all of this work into the number of beaver pelts he might secure here and the number of dollars these would represent. A hard, unimaginative little man was Whitey.

As he watched, a brown head appeared in the water beyond the lodge; beside it came up four smaller heads. They stayed quite still for a few minutes then moved toward some stones near the shore. Presently five beavers were sprawled out in the sunshine combing their beautiful fur. Whitey's eyes glittered. Now he had his information for use when the fur-trapping season came. Noiselessly he backed away and vanished in the woods.

The mother bear, with two new cubs, occasionally crossed from the neighboring valley to hunt berries around the pond. She would always take a look at the old rotting timbers as if thinking of the time when the pond was not there and she had chased the beaver into the burrow. Now that the little fish were rapidly growing large in the deep water, she had her eye on them too. Once she climbed on the lodge and, with her nose pressed against the ventilator, drew in long breaths delicious with the promising odor of live beaver; but she knew that now the beavers were safe. Her inquisitive cubs pranced up to sniff at the same place. One of them clawed at the tightly packed mass of sticks, but could not even budge a single branch; yes, the beavers had done their work well.

A drought in early September made the creek so low that the pond lacked enough water to keep it full. At once the father beaver made a trip into the woods to look for more springs. With narrow ditches he linked two little ones with the canal that was dug to the cottonwoods, and led them into the pond through holes he made in the canal dams. At the same time, as an extra support to the big, main dam of the pond, he started a third one directly below the second. Now he felt it well to add a layer of brush to the main dam itself, thus raising the pond water a few inches and making it easier to float logs from the shallow edges.

The food supply had been increased by the growth of spatterdocks and water lilies in the mud-bottom coves of the pond. Seeds of these plants had been brought by water birds which had eaten some in other ponds and, being unable to digest them, had dropped a few here and

there. Cattails and calamus plants shot up at the water's edge from the same cause. The roots of all of these were eatable.

When the pond had first been made, many small trees in the flooded places had been killed by the water burying their roots from the air. These had remained standing in the water like long leafless sticks. Many had been broken away by the ice, and those that were left now

109

rotted and fell into the water to lie in the bottom and give more protection to the fish. Trout grew large and fat in the pond.

In November the beavers heard sounds that disturbed them. Voices of men, crashing of brush, the thud of heavy boots. Day after day, while they cowered in their lodge these noises continued. After a time strange little wooden posts appeared in the woods and around the

pond. Little square pieces of paper here and there were fastened to the trees. The beavers did not understand what it was all about, but they were disturbed and worried. The father and the mother spent much time at night watching the little posts and the other marks of man. They dared not go far ashore. But when deep snow fell, the men came no more. Old Whitey, the trapper, had sneaked up the creek, seen the square pieces of paper with the writing on them and with much angry mumbling under his breath about " No trespassing " signs, had gone too.

Winter once more held the mountains in its white grip, again the little wisp of vapor rose from the snow-coated lodge, and the travelling foxes or the bobcat stopped on the mound to sniff longingly and listen to the gentle murmurings of the beaver family.

In the spring there were three new baby beavers. This time the two oldest youngsters, now two years old, as well as the father, had been made to leave and seek burrows, so that there would be room for the latest arrivals. And then, in the midst of the joy of beautiful, happy days came another great change.

XI

THE JOURNEY

ALMOST as suddenly as the coming of a storm, houses
were again being built on the edge of Tinker's Creek,
workmen's shanties, machine shops, sheds for the storage
of cement. A road now led up the valley and bore rat-
tling, roaring trucks up the steep hills. Engineers with
better tools, but no greater skill than the beavers, were
preparing to build an immense dam that would store the
good water of the whole little valley and pipe it to settle-
ments many miles away.

On all sides sounded the fateful blow of the axe on
living wood, cutting down the food supply of the flat tails

in their poor little pond. The beavers, peace and quiet-loving woods folk, could not stand this noise and fuss and danger. The barking of the dogs at night and worst of all the lights gave them no rest even after the noise of the day had died down.

And so they decided to move. But where to? Upstream was too little water as well as unknown country, so downstream they would go. Quietly, one night, the whole family started out together. The mother led. Behind her came the three youngest, still mere kittens, then the father followed by the four half grown youngsters and last of all the two eldest children. It was a sorrowful little procession.

At the big main dam which had represented so much toil, the father stopped to sniff and look around at all his work and the little pond he loved so well. But there was no turning back. As if from habit he patted a small leak in the structure, pressed down a stick or two and then shuffled over the rim and turned his back on the familiar old timbers that still stood as a relic of Si Tinker's original work.

Keeping to the stream and watching for enemies with all their bright little eyes the band of eleven continued onwards, rarely stopping and never hesitating. On and on, until the kittens whimpered and could scarcely move their short little legs.

Then where the high creek bank had been undermined

by the water and tipped over, forming a good hiding place, they stopped to rest. Past them all day thundered the trucks without the drivers having the slightest inkling of the huddled group under the bank.

At nightfall they started out again, the little ones stiff and sore but uncomplaining as they crawled around and over the hard, sharp stones. Ahead, the father and mother had the expectation of finding the old pond, with others of their kind, but the youngsters knew nothing of this and followed, blindly trusting in their elders.

But where the old pond had been there was now no

114

water except the little creek. The dam was broken open, the place deserted and all grown up with weeds. Here and there were the stakes to which trappers had fastened the traps of steel which had caught and drowned the furry ones, one by one, until the last was gone.

Blankly the old beavers looked around and wondered. They knew that something terrible had happened, that the place was dangerous. On again, this time in entirely new country but with the creek growing just a little bit deeper as it picked up one spring after another.

Now they were in farm land where open fields bordered the water and cattle grazed or lay in groups. New sights, new smells, new perils, and still the beavers travelled on.

Suddenly the mother stopped. Day had broken and two fishermen were wading in the creek ahead. They were moving upstream, casting their lines in front of them as they walked. In the light breeze the man scent cut across the creek like a barrier.

" Look! " cried one. " An army of huge rats! "

" No, they're otter! They must be otter! "

Then, as the beavers turned and tried to run upstream, the men saw their flat tails and knew what they were.

" Let's catch the little ones! " they shouted.

Up the creek bed they ran. The beavers splashed through the shallow water, ducking and dodging, with the two men floundering clumsily after them. It was

116

hard enough for the old ones, and the youngest had little chance. There was no pond or pool in which to dive, no cover in which to hide. One struggling kitten after another was captured and thrust into the wicker fish creels.

And the shouts of the fishermen brought three boys on the run from the neighboring farmhouse. They had never before seen live wild beaver. Excitement overcame their better sense. It never occurred to them to leave the poor furry ones alone.

The father beaver had one idea; it was to reach the shelter of a bridge he had passed under some time before. While the men were chasing and cornering the seven younger ones he, followed by the mother and the two eldest, was rushing back to this hiding place. In vain' the boys yelled and tried to head them off or turn them back. The father was a formidable looking animal and he was strong. Fiercely he drove toward the bridge, and behind him still struggled the remaining three.

That they all reached the bridge was almost a miracle. First the father, then his mate and last of all the two biggest children. And under the low bridge, in the foundations of the roadbed, were hollows dug by muskrats and washed larger by water, perfect hiding places. In vain the boys poked in sticks and stamped about; for a time, at least, the beavers were safe.

In the evening, when all was quiet and the light very dim before the rising of the moon, they came out of hiding and ran upstream until they reached a pool in which it was possible to dive. Feeling more safe here, they searched the banks for twigs and roots to nibble, finding enough for a fair meal.

These four could travel fast and they were still very much scared, but none knew just where to go. It ended in the parents remaining to search for their lost young while the two well grown children, who were at the ad-

venturous age, continued the journey downstream. They parted doubtfully, with many looks backward. And from that point the youngsters began to leave their scent on little dabs of mud wherever they stopped along the way.

It was well that rain began to fall and keep some of their enemies at home.

The two young males reached a brook which flowed into the creek. Here, finding beaver sign, they joyfully travelled up this new waterway until they reached a prosperous beaver colony in a well hidden pond. Like their father, they later won as mates two pretty, young lady beavers with whom they journeyed further upstream to undertake new pond building where the birch groves promised food aplenty and where there was as yet no sign of man.

For two nights the mother beaver would not leave the section of the creek where the fishermen had caught her kittens. While the father waited in the stream on guard she would climb on the bank, sit up on her hind legs and look about, occasionally giving a plaintive call that would have moved the heart of any fisherman had he heard it. But the men were far away and the kittens in a wire enclosure where they were kept as pets and well cared for, though their liberty was gone.

And at last the two old beavers gave up the search. Gone was their desire to hunt new country. They deserted the cheerless hole under the bridge and travelled back to their own little pond. And there it lay, just as they had left it, with the lodge still hidden among the alders on the point of land, and only the lights from the new cabins to warn them that man was still at hand.

XII

MAN COMES AGAIN

ONCE more the beaver pair had the lodge to themselves. Their children were gone, and the muskrats had moved away; but they, at least, were still together. While the mother beaver arranged the bedding and fluffed it up to dry more thoroughly, the father left the lodge and, paddling slowly around the pond, noted more little white posts, some of them close to the water's edge and several at the side of the main dam. Here were the claim posts of man, he thought, just like the little dabs of mud he left on the sand bars to carry his scent. They were increasing in number and hemming in his little pond as well as his feeding ground.

MAN COMES AGAIN

He turned to the shore and closely examined one of the posts. Its man scent angered him. What were these little posts anyway? Cautiously he gnawed one and found it made of wood with a thin coating of bad tasting white substance. Biting further he found the wood soft and easily cut. In a minute the post was no longer there: the beaver had gnawed through it and carried the end to help fill in a weak place of the dam. Four other posts vanished that night.

Every day the engineers put up more posts, and every night they vanished or remained as mere stumps. The work of preparing for the concrete dam was at a standstill, held in check by one poor beaver.

The engineers were not bad fellows. They admired the remarkable industry of beavers, but could not allow it forever to interfere with their own plans.

" The old ' chisel-tooth ' who lives to cut down the survey markers must go," they said. So on the day following four workmen were ordered to attack the lodge with pick and shovel. Down the main water exit hurried the scared beavers, and under water they swam to the old burrow in the bank. The men hacked lustily, but in an hour had not broken a hole in the lodge roof. The tightly piled brush, logs, roots and mud defeated them just as it had the bears and other animals. They sent for axes and then chopped the roof away, bit by bit, finally reaching the big pile of soft bark and grass which still carried the shapes of the two who had been sleeping there side by side so comfortably.

The men examined everything with astonishment. They disliked their task of destroying such a home.

That night the two beavers found their work of months and years scattered all over the pond, and next day the engineers had lost more little posts, until they saw parts of them floating on the quiet water.

Now war was declared in earnest. The chisel-toothed ones had to be found and destroyed or chased away. But since the beaver pond was a help to the men at this stage of their work they did not wish to tear down the dam. Not knowing much about traps, they employed Whitey, the trapper, and humanely promised extra pay if the beaver or beavers were captured unhurt.

And Whitey, well knowing his business, went about his work that very day. First he chopped a shallow hole in the top of the dam, then in this, under the flowing water, he set two steel traps with jaws and springs strong enough to hold a beaver by the foot. The traps were fastened to stakes driven into the dam.

No sooner had the hole begun to let the pond flow out than the beavers noticed the water becoming lower in the end of their burrow. This was such a serious thing that they did not rest any longer and could scarcely wait for night to come and make it safe for them to go out and repair the dam. Only too well they knew that it had a leak, but they did not know the cause.

It was the father beaver who ventured out first. He lay quietly on the surface of the lowered pond and, in the starlight, studied the shore more carefully than usual for sign of any enemy. He did not see Whitey crouching among the bushes on the shore. At length, he swam slowly to the break in the dam and found out what it needed in the way of mending. Then diving, he swam

along the bottom until he found a chunky, sunken log that once had been part of the woodpile. This he carried to the dam and poked into the break. But it was so heavy that to place it properly he had to climb on to the dam itself and pull the log.

Whitey, watching from his hiding place, scarcely breathed as the big beaver came out of the water, shook some of the drops out of his neck fur, and then moved forward. He was only a distance of inches from the first trap. Then some instinct or scent warned him. He moved now as if stepping on eggshells. He touched the trap. But no sooner did that first front foot feel the trip-pan give under its weight than he leaped aside in instant panic. Just too late! The steel jaws jumped after his foot and caught him by the toes.

With a yell of triumph Whitey rushed forward. The beaver plunged into the water, pulling the trap to the end of its chain. Seizing the chain the man tried to jerk him out; he braced his feet and pulled with all his might against the sixty pounds of fighting animal struggling for its freedom. The beaver was twisting among the logs and brush that stuck out from the dam. He braced against these, regardless of pain, and almost held his own in the unfair battle. Gradually, however, he had to give way, an inch or two at a time. He knew he was losing.

Suddenly he twisted his muscular body around a heavy branch and, firmly braced for the moment, turned to tear at the trap with his teeth. Never before had he felt hard, ungiving steel. Desperately then he gnawed at his foot, ripping with those great chisel teeth. Whitey, too, pulled all the harder. Flesh and bone could not stand against this. Snap went two toes. Another great, painful tug and the beaver was free, swimming wildly for the burrow. Whitey, caught off his balance, went over backwards and plunged head first into the pool below the dam, barely missing a dangerous boulder.

When the stout little man climbed out, all soaked and furious, there was scarcely a ripple left on the pond. He stood for a few moments looking at his traps. That night he had been defeated, he must go in and change his clothes; the beaver, he thought, would not return anyway. And so he hurried toward the cabin lights, dragging his traps with him.

On the following morning the engineers found their stake numbered 24 missing and the dam perfectly repaired. In the fresh mass of mud and sticks they caught sight of the number 24 on a well chewed bit of wood. Again old Chisel-Tooth had come and left his mark.

XIII

LONELINESS

THE front foot of the big beaver and its tendons had been so badly torn that before long the leg all the way into the shoulder was a mass of pain. On the following day he could scarcely move it and soon became so full of fever all over, that he lay in the rough bed at the end of the burrow and scarcely moved during day or night. Had his companion not been there to bring in twigs and water lily roots he might easily have starved. Though she did not know just what was wrong, she stayed with him, whimpering her sympathy, arranging the bedding material, and fussing about the dark little earthy room as if never sure that it was comfortable enough.

The fact that again the water was low in the pond did not mean very much to them during those first bad days. But when gradually the fever subsided and her mate

126

could move about just a little the mother beaver began to think more seriously about the dam. The water certainly was low, dangerously so. Therefore, that night she paddled out to look for the cause of the trouble.

Now it happened that Whitey had almost despaired of ever again seeing the beavers. After three nights of lonely, useless watching he had decided to let the traps stay set at the dam merely on the slim chance that one of the animals might return. He had had enough of hiding in the bushes.

So when the mother beaver came with a stick to begin repairs and was caught by the foot in almost exactly the same way as her mate had been, no one was at hand to stop her suffering. It was not long, however, before a little white dog that belonged to one of the engineers came sniffing along the water's edge. Being alone he was very timid, and being a house pet he knew little about the woods and the wild creatures. Trotting over the dam he suddenly was faced by a furry creature larger than himself, which rose up from the very mud on which he was stepping.

With a yowl of fright the little white dog leaped away, and every hair of his back was on end. But the furry creature did not chase him as he had expected. It merely strained toward the pond and made a clanking noise as if chained. So after a few moments of doubt, the dog slowly came back, fairly quivering with fright, but over-

come with curiosity. He sprang away whenever the
beaver moved, but soon saw that this strange creature
was unable to follow him. Then at once his courage grew
and burst from him in shrill barking. He had found a
very strange creature and he wanted the whole world to
come and see it and know what a wonderful dog he was,
even though so small.

There was such a noise from the little fellow that the
workmen were disturbed in the cabins and Whitey himself waked out of a heavy sleep. The trapper guessed
what had happened. Carrying a large sack he came
hopping to the pond in his blue, extra length night
clothes, but this time found his beaver.

LONELINESS

In vain the wild creature tried to break away. She was not as strong as her mate and lacked the recklessness which had made him tear his own foot. Whitey soon had his prize in the bag and the trap safely removed from her foot and reset. At the cabin he shook her out of the sack into a box all ready for shipment by motor to a city zoo. Then he went happily back to bed.

And though there was no one who could tell the father beaver what had happened, he had heard the noise and knew that since his mate did not at once return to hide, something had happened to her. Weak as he was he swam out before morning and looked all around the pond. In front of the dam he floated for a long time. There was the danger point as he had reason to know, and there, with the scent of his enemy, the trapper, he found the last trace of her.

But still he did not understand. Afraid to land he drifted about, wondering and hoping. And while he waited there a cottontail rabbit came hopping slowly across the dam only to stop suddenly and bolt back. She too had caught the strange mingling of scents that could mean just one thing—danger—and her action was additional warning.

As light gradually grew in the sky and the day birds awoke and began to call to each other before beginning to hunt for food, the beaver quietly swam back to the burrow. He had eaten nothing, and his bad leg, water-

129

soaked and stiff with cold, ached dully as he limped up the dark incline.

Another night came. The beaver had stayed all day crouching in the burrow, waiting. Now he pushed himself into the water and again examined the pond, the bank, and last of all the dam, but without going close to the trap. There was no fresh sign of his mate; but he saw the little white dog come hopefully looking for more sport, and tangled him up with fright by slapping his great tail on the water with a noise like an explosion.

When everything was quiet again, the beaver suddenly started straight upstream, scarcely looking to right or left as he followed what he thought must be the only route that his mate could have taken. She and he knew the dangers that were to be encountered downstream, and neither she nor he would have left the friendly water to go overland. So upstream he slowly travelled, searching for some sign of her.

Even here there were fresh marks of man, trees cut down, roads and little bridges constructed. Most of the wild creatures, including the bobcat and the bears, had been scared away. There was food enough, however, and under the overhanging banks or behind tree roots there were fairly snug and safe sleeping places. During the ten days that the beaver was searching along the creek and the tinkling little brooks that were its tributaries, his scars healed and he grew much stronger.

But he was no happier. There seemed to be no sign of his mate. So at last he turned back. This happened on a misty night late in July when, except for their misfortunes, he and his family might have been happily playing around their little pond enjoying the summer weather and the luxury of the season of plenty.

When finally he approached the pond, sliding along with the current between the mossy stones, a queer scent suddenly filled the air. It was the smell of dead and dying water plants and of rich mud laid bare by water being drawn off—the pond was gone. For a few minutes he stood in the stream amid the desolation of black mud and looked at things. The dam was down too and in its place stood a high framework of yellow boards which would hold the concrete poured by man. On all sides, too, the remaining timber was being cut.

While the brown bats he knew so well dodged about his head after the insects that he stirred into flight, the beaver moved upstream again. His whole mind seemed shattered. On the sand bars he looked for mud pats just as if he had not been past there a little time before. At the first big bend he dug behind a section of fallen bank. There he made a little room and stayed all alone listening day after day to the great water reservoir being constructed far down the creek. At night he came out and sat on a flat rock in the water, always on the lookout for

131

his mate. Occasionally a plaintive call escaped him, but usually he was quiet.

In September the reservoir was completed. The water began to accumulate until it backed up to the beaver's new home. It made a fine lake around which he could swim for an hour without coming back to his starting point. Near the left bank was a little round island on which he sometimes sat and waited just as he had done

on the flat stone up the creek. Brush and boards had collected on this; perhaps they gave him the idea of building a lodge, for one night he went to work. Digging a burrow from the deep water into the island he heaped litter of all kinds on the place where the tunnel came out of the dry ground.

Some nights he was half hearted about it, but on others he worked with all his might until the lodge grew to formidable size. And inside, the room he made was for two and the bedding he shredded so carefully was for her for whom he always waited.

The engineers had expected to remove the island, but when the beaver took possession, and when, evening after evening, they saw the lonely old fellow sitting on his roof looking hopefully for his mate, they did not have the heart to do it. Old Chisel-Tooth, they saw, had changed; he had resigned himself to fate and advancing civilization. No longer were the little white stakes on the banks carried away, or their work interfered with in any way. Fear of man also seemed to have gone. It was just as if the beaver no longer cared.

He did not ask for sympathy, but somehow his loneliness and his bravery about it made everyone feel sorry for him and somewhat ashamed. After all, they had come and spoiled all his work, changed his happy valley, maimed him, taken even his mate; and here was he, still staying on the spot, never losing his hope and faith.

At length, unable to bear it any longer, they worked out a plan to secure a companion for him. A female beaver was secured from a fur farm in Canada, brought to the reservoir and ferried out to the island on a boat.

The water was very still, and the sun had set. The new beaver, confused by strange sights and scents, had stepped timidly from her box and remained crouching near the lodge.

XIV

THE FLOOD

Over the pond the stars and a sickle moon gave a faint
light. Suddenly a flat head appeared in the water not
far from the island. Silently old Chisel-Tooth was looking at the stranger. He dived and came up at another
spot. Then there was a streak in the water as he churned
forward and almost threw himself on to the island.

The new beaver started to retreat, and in that moment
he caught her scent and knew instantly that she was not
his mate. There he stopped. His head, which had been
thrown back, drooped now almost to the ground. He
still looked at her, but would not go an inch forward
though she moved coyly around the island in front of
him. Presently he climbed on top of the lodge, ignored

134

the other entirely, and resumed his watch for her whom he could not forget. It was evident to those who watched that Chisel-Tooth would always be faithful.

The new beaver never gained admittance to the lodge, and, being a shiftless, ranch-raised creature, she did not know what to do. So she moped about the reservoir until finally the men again caught her. Another brilliant idea had occurred to them.

Placing the beaver in her box two of them took her a long trip by automobile. They returned that night in excellent spirits and with another beaver which they had secured in exchange. This one was larger and more beautifully furred. Her eyes had the sensitive, gentle look of the wild. Carrying the box down to the water's edge they released her at the very time when old Chisel-Tooth usually came out to mount his watch tower. But this time he was late.

The strange beaver, after dashing away from the men, had swum around the island, walked all over it, and then again launched herself into the water. Excitedly she was searching for something or someone. And while she swam about, another head appeared on the calm surface.

Scarcely a dozen feet apart the two animals floated in the pond, looking at each other. Both seemed afraid to move, as if dreading that their eyes deceived them. But something, perhaps only the unseen current in the water, was drawing them together. Slowly the distance

135

lessened, yet neither stirred. Ten feet—eight feet—four feet—they were finally face to face.

Chisel-Tooth put up a front foot—the unhurt one—like a little hand and ran it gently over the other's nose and down the side of her brown head. He seemed in a kind of daze. And when he raised the left foot, the broken one that lacked two toes, the other beaver rubbed her nose against it, again and again, ever so lightly.

On the bank, where several people had quietly gathered, a subdued whisper arose; then slowly they moved away, almost on tiptoe. The Zoo had freed its most popular captive to give back to old Chisel-Tooth his beautiful mate.

And what a change now took place on the island. Before the last flock of summer birds had gone on the way south, a great cap of mud covered the now prosperous lodge, dug, carried there, and patted down flat by four willing little hands, all working together.

The visiting supervisor looked at it and shook his head. He had not been with the engineers.

"There's no telling what those beavers will do next," he said to the watchman, who was the only man remaining in the shanties.

"When the winter goes, I think you had better chase them away and remove the island. They might decide to let the water out of the reservoir, and I believe they could do it!"

THE FLOOD

But before the winter ice shut things in, a final rain-storm swept the mountains and made one of those wild torrents out of Tinker's Creek which years before had nearly swept the beavers from their home. So violent was the storm that for a day and a night the watchman did not venture far from his house. Logs and tree trunks floated the length of the reservoir and jammed against the concrete dam or thundered over it.

On the evening of the second day the watchman noticed something queer about the water. A stream was gushing through a hole torn in the earth bank at one end; the reservoir had sprung a leak.

A frantic call for help went over the wire to the village miles below. At any moment the hole might grow much larger, the entire mass of concrete be undermined and, without its supports, go crashing down the valley with a mass of water which would destroy everything in its path.

Trucks, hastily manned, started up the mountain road but were blocked almost at once by fallen trees and washouts. Rain poured down. The night, like black pitch, shut off the way to the rescuers, who at length gave it up and turned back.

The people of the valley were too worried to sleep, and in many houses remained fully clothed, praying that the reservoir dam would hold. Morning found a whole town on its way up the mountain road. The storm had ceased, but Tinker's Creek roared beside them louder than ever, rolling the boulders in a great yellow mass of seething water and foam.

At length they cleared the way to the top and approached the dam. On the run now, carrying their shovels, those in the lead came within sight of the reservoir and caught the glint of the long stretch of water and the fall of the yellow flood over the spillway. They stopped, mute with surprise. Surely nothing seemed wrong here. The dam stood as tight and strong as the day it was built.

They met the watchman coming down the path. His face was all smiles, and there was something triumphant in his manner as he told them to come with him and look. They filed down to the water's edge where the concrete joined the mountain and where a great gash had been torn by the flood. Here had been the leak that threatened a valley, and here the excited men saw a tight mass of sticks and logs forming a stoppage which even they could not have surpassed. It almost seemed as if the materials were woven together and then strengthened with sods.

" Did you do that? " cried one of the surprised villagers to the watchman.

" Not I," he answered, pulling out a branch marked freshly by the teeth of a beaver.

" Well! What do you think of that! " gasped the villager.

THE FLOOD

They looked toward the island where many of them had often seen the beavers' lodge, but it was not there. Only yellow water with lines of dirty bubbles and foam floating on its surface.

Nor did they find the beavers. Whether the furry ones had gone away that night or been swept over the dam in the midst of their work, no one could tell. It was evident that when the two had noticed the water begin to fall in the entrance of their lodge, they had gone out to the rescue of the dam just as they had always done in response to that remarkable instinct which had carried their race down through the ages. Probably then the driftwood and current had begun to tear away the lodge, or perhaps the beavers themselves did this in their frantic need of materials, for they had put into the end of the dam a large amount of brush and roots which, at such short notice, could only have come from the lodge itself.

In any event, they had done their work well. The water no longer could tear at unprotected earth and threaten to undermine the concrete.

"It's just as well we didn't get here last night," said the leader of the men. "All of us together could not have done an underwater job as good as that! And in the dark too!"

But where the brave beavers went perhaps will never be known. People searched, but no fresh trace of them was ever again seen. They were the last of their vanishing clan in that part of the country. Man had come and they had gone.

In front of the big reservoir, now the home of tame ducks and swans, there stands today a metal sign which reads:

" Beaver Lake. Named in honor of a pair of beavers who saved the homes and perhaps the lives of residents in the valley of Tinker's Creek."

And in each little woodsman's cottage and farmhouse the children have collected twigs and scraps of old wood which were cleverly peeled and marked by sharp teeth in those happy years long past. The proudest among these children is a boy whose father had saved for him an engineer's little white stake cut through by the powerful jaws of none other than old Chisel-Tooth.